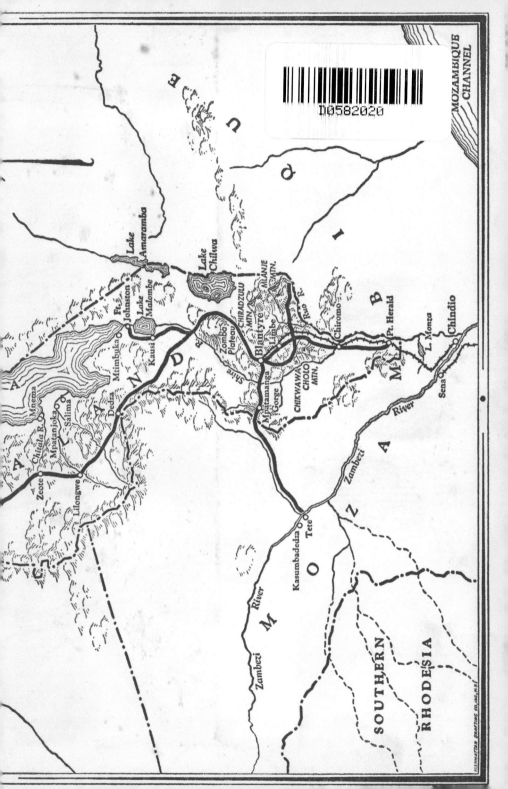

I DRANK THE ZAMBEZI

Books by Arthur Loveridge

I DRANK THE ZAMBEZI

TOMORROW'S A HOLIDAY

MANY HAPPY DAYS I'VE SQUANDERED

REPTILES OF THE PACIFIC WORLD

I Drank the

ZAMBEZI

ARTHUR LOVERIDGE

HARPER & BROTHERS NEW YORK

Library of Congress catalog card number: 52-11691

To Miss Hilda Sloan
    truck driver extraordinary
    this book is affectionately dedicated

CONTENTS

ILLUSTRATIONS

ix

FOREWORD

"Pit . . . pat . . . pit . . . pat." Sometimes slow, now fast, at first, in front, then close behind. An erratic yet pervading sound in the depths of the montane forest, where it is past midnight, and a cloud laden with moisture sucked up from yesterday's sun-baked swamps has come to rest among the evergreen foliage on the mountaintop. Precipitation resulting from the collision with the cool leaves has set in, and the burdened cloud is shedding its surplus water in great drops that drip from the green leaves above to the brown ones carpeting the forest floor below. But the underlying spongy leaf mold is already fairly saturated so the moisture seeps downhill until it encounters the water table. Then, its progress temporarily thwarted, it creates a soggy marshy spot that gives rise to a trickle, and so a stream is born.

At first flowing brown through peaty channels, the water clears itself cascading among the boulders and rocks where it meets and merges with other streams hastening downward to the distant sea two thousand miles away. Already it is a boon to weary travelers who pause to rest beside the sparkling water and wash the dust from tired black feet. A rendezvous for African women, each bearing on her head a heavy, homemade pot of clay that must be filled twice daily. Despite these recurrent raids by thousands of women on its very substance, the stream continues to grow in size and power till it becomes a river on which men travel for days together in canoes laboriously hewn from solid twenty-foot tree trunks. Presently, rushing madly through restricting rock-girt canyons, the river plunges over falls greater than Niagara, and onward until free once more.

With the leveling off of the land the river's pace shows signs of slackening so that countless crocodiles and hundreds of hippopotamuses have made it their home. Here and there upon its banks clusters of huts are occupied by those engaged in fishing or basket-making, weaving their wares from the wealth of reeds and sedges growing in the shallows of sluggish stretches. When the bountiful river that supplies so many of their needs flows close to a village it is presented with the garbage. On goes the river scouring the soil from its banks at every bend, undercutting them day after day until they collapse into the current, staining it brown. Browner and broader it grows each year, annually augmented by the break-ing of the heavy monsoon rains that make a rivulet of every foot-path. At such times a flood of water surges down each dry watercourse, carrying with it the dust and débris of the past seven months, hastening to swell that mighty volume of water that the dwellers on its banks call Zambezi.

This is the same Zambezi that, pouring its accumulated silt into the sea, browns the Indian Ocean as much as thirty miles from land to the periodic puzzlement of steamship passengers. Truly a subject for reflection when one realizes that this brown sediment, which is annually stripped from thousands of square miles by monsoon flooding, is the fertile topsoil so vital to the welfare of the African peasant.

A magical time is the onset of these rains, for at the second or third downpour heralding the end of the enervating dry season, myriads of insects appear. Awakening from their long estivation, the masculine members of most species of frogs forgather in the freshly formed pools and swamps to start summoning their mates with a noisy vehemence that is often deafening. The sonorous, sawing sound made by the Square-marked Toads (*Bufo*) is soon joined by a great variety of equally strange calls. Some resemble the "tink-tink" of fairy hammers falling on tiny anvils (*Rana*), the cry of others is like water bubbles breaking resonantly (*Kassina*), while various kinds of brilliantly colored Sedge Frogs (*Hyperolius*) con-trive to inflate their tenuous vocal sacs to bursting point before releasing the imprisoned air with such a "snap" that it sounds like the crack of a small whip.

Of these sedge frogs several strikingly handsome species were dis-covered and described just over a century ago by a young German naturalist, Wilhelm Peters by name, who ascended the Zambezi to

Tete, 290 miles by river from the coast. Thirty-eight years later colored illustrations, apparently an artist's interpretation based on Peters' original brief descriptions of the frogs he had found at Tete, were published.[1] In the present century the names proposed by Peters so long ago have been applied to various frogs—sometimes erroneously. Hoping to dissipate uncertainties and establish the status of these species on a more satisfactory basis by procuring fresh material, I longed to visit Tete, planning to reach there when the advent of the monsoon rains should lure the little amphibians from their estivating quarters.

Away to the north of the Zambezi lies the Nyasaland Protectorate, a land where mountainous plateaus rise rather abruptly from the torrid plains. Formerly the mountains were clothed in virgin forests of which only pitiful remnants remain today. Few creatures that have become adapted to life in the cool evergreen forests survive the destruction of their habitat. The mammals and birds have received considerable attention, but no time was to be lost if we were ever to know what reptiles and amphibians dwelt there. I hoped the two projects might be combined.

To bear the entire burden of such an investigation was beyond the means of Harvard's Museum of Comparative Zoology, so taking up my begging bowl I solicited help from several of the great foundations that on former occasions had come to my aid. Eventually the Trustees of the American Philosophical Society's Penrose Fund agreed to meet half the expenses if the Museum would find the rest. To this my chief, Professor A. S. Romer, readily acquiesced, for from the outset he had given the proposal his wholehearted support. So, at long last, the way was clear for me to proceed with the endless arrangements that must be made before embarking on a nine-months safari under canvas.

In due course these difficulties were surmounted and I set out, accompanied, as on previous expeditions, by my wife, Mary. This time we were fortunate in being joined by a volunteer truck driver —my sister-in-law, Miss Hilda Sloan—who defrayed her own ex-

[1] Wilhelm Peters, "Naturwissenschaftliche Reise nach Mossambique auf Befehl seiner Majestät des Königs Friedrich Wilhelm IV in den Jahren 1842 bis 1848 ausgeführt. Zoologie 3. Amphibien." (1882. Berlin, 40, pp. i-xv, 1-191, pls. i-xxx.)

penses for the privilege of attempting something she had never done before! In the following pages she is referred to as Billy, but when necessity demands mention of both my companions, for the sake of brevity they are referred to as M. & B. The opportunity is taken of thanking my wife for reading over the typescript of this book and making many suggestions for its improvement.

I am grateful to my wife and Miss Sloan for all the non-aerial photographic illustrations used in the book; and to the American Geographical Society of New York for permission to reproduce the three views by Dr. Mary Light from Dr. Richard U. Light's book *Focus on Africa.*

ARTHUR LOVERIDGE

I DRANK THE ZAMBEZI

I

First Glimpse of Zambezi—
Blantyre Attained

VOYAGERS in Nyasaland must take leave of the Indian Ocean at the port of Beira, into which the *R.M.S. Llandovery Castle* was moving one sultry July morning in 1948. It was a Saturday and my waking worry had been whether the contagion of a five-day work week had spread from the States to Mozambique. If the banks did not open we should be in a predicament for the limited amount of currency we had been allowed to take out of England was almost gone. Nobody on board appeared to know for certain. So, after passing the immigration officials, Mary and I waited about impatiently for the gangway to be lowered. When at long last this was done and securely lashed in position by the bosun, I inquired if we might go ashore. "The ship has not been cleared so far as I know," he answered as he turned away to some other task. Promptly Mary, being the less law-abiding, walked swiftly down the unguarded gangway. Meekly I followed, though momentarily expecting to be hailed and halted. Fortunately the decks were mostly deserted as the bugle had just summoned our fellow passengers to breakfast.

For a mile we hurried through Beira's busy docks, were passed by the customs guards at the dock gates, and finally found the Standard Bank of South Africa open for business. Having exchanged our traveler's checks for nearly a thousand escudos, we felt sufficiently affluent to engage a taxi to drive us back to the ship. Hot, but happy at having successfully negotiated the first hurdle, we hurried down to the dining saloon for a late breakfast. At our table were sitting strangers, one of whom, much to my surprise, addressed me by name. He introduced himself as the Union-Castle Company's local representative, and remarked that awaiting me at his office was a telegram stating our truck had not reached Blantyre.

With pessimistic intuition I had almost expected this. The truck in question, on whose welfare all our plans depended, had been shipped from New York more than four months before. On previous expeditions, when it was necessary to shift equipment from one mountain foot to another, it had been possible to engage a lorry. But in postwar Nyasaland, so it was said, trucks were scarce and in such demand for carrying produce from plantation to railhead that I would stand small chance of getting one except at competitively prohibitive prices. Under the circumstances the Chrysler Corporation had come to the rescue and, at short notice, assembled a Dodge to our specifications, capable of carrying four tons.

But no sooner was the truck at sea than I received word from the Nyasaland Customs telling me that it was improbable any motor vehicles would be able to enter Nyasaland for many months as the bridge across the Shire[1] River had been swept away by floods. There was still no bridge across the Shire, said the agent, and the train by which we must leave Beira on Monday evening would stop at the river. He doubted if we could find accommodation in Beira over the week end as all hotels were fully booked by passengers waiting to embark on the Monday. Only that morning, though without success, he had endeavored to secure a room for someone at the Savoy, Beira's sole British hotel.

Obviously I had better return to town to seek quarters immediately, even though the customs would close at 11:00 A.M. I rose and was going to fetch my hat from the cabin when an English-speaking Portuguese handed me a letter. It was from Messrs. J. M. Barnett & Company, the firm that had cleared and forwarded the truck and equipment. They said the note was being presented by their repre-

[1] Pronounced "Sheery," as in "cheery"!

sentative who would facilitate my passage through the customs. When I explained to him the more urgent necessity of securing week-end accommodation, he at once departed on his cycle. Great was my relief when he returned to say that though the Hotel Avenida was full, he had been able to engage two rooms which were being vacated at noon.

It was near noon when we reached the Avenida, which appeared to have been much neglected during the war years but was now in process of being redecorated throughout. Things were still shabby in the old wing to which we were conducted apologetically by the new manageress, recently arrived from Paris. From the uncarpeted corridor a door led into each bedroom, while opposite it a second door opened onto a broad balcony, embellished by ornamental iron-work, overhanging the busy thoroughfare below.

Observing that none of the doors had keys, I asked Madame for them. "It ees not necessary," she replied airily, "all our boys are very serious." By which, I assumed, she meant honest. It would have been nice to share such unqualified confidence, but having read much about the postwar peccadilloes of Africans in neighboring territories, I felt something more substantial than flimsy five-cent bolts on the doors would contribute to sounder sleep.

We went down to the lofty and scrupulously clean dining hall where an excellent lunch was served by African waiters. Many of them were decidedly good-looking and all appeared happy and contented; unfortunately they spoke no Swahili but some understood a little English. With one exception, besides ourselves, the guests appeared to be Portuguese. After the meal when Mary and Billy adjourned to their room to rest, they were somewhat disconcerted by sundry guests sauntering up and down the balcony and looking in through the unshuttered windows.

I had other plans, for my attitude toward a thriving township like Beira is slightly different from that of most people. No sooner am I settled in such a place than I make every effort to get out again. For me Beira's chief claim to fame was the fact that a certain burrowing frog and toad had first been discovered there over forty years before. It was improbable that I could find fossorial amphibians on Avenida Avenue on a hot Saturday afternoon, so I decided to concentrate on two kinds of lizards reported from Beira but of which there were no representatives in the Museum of Comparative Zoology. Hailing a taxi I asked the driver what he would charge to transport me to where I could find lizards. He did not think it could be done for less than a hundred escudos, so I left him and set off on foot to find the country.

However uncongenial the climate or unpromising the site, a good anchorage will tempt someone to start unloading his ship. So among the muddy mangrove swamps and sun-scorched sand flats the teeming seaport of Beira had arisen. Obviously it was still growing, and fast, for on every side as I headed inland buildings were going up—huge modern structures of steel and concrete, in addition to countless villas. Indeed, as elsewhere in this postwar world, it seemed as if the builders were losing the competition—so acute was the housing shortage.

These reflections were banished by a small lizard that, seeing me coming along the avenue, adroitly slipped around the trunk on which it was basking. Thereafter, passing Natives, of whom there was a steady stream, eyed me curiously as singlehanded I surrounded tree after tree, pouncing on the lizards with a soft pad of cotton until I had captured half a dozen. My object was to ascertain whether the scales on the underside of their tails were transversely enlarged—when they would be referable to *Lygodactylus g. grotei*—or homogenous like a tesselated pavement—in which case they must be called *Lygodactylus capensis*. Both species had been recorded from Beira, which seemed unlikely, and I hoped an examination of my captives would reveal if this was really the case. Alas, though inclining toward the tesselated type, the arrangement of their scales was somewhat intermediate. While furnishing a possible explanation why both kinds had been reported from Beira, it left unsettled the relationship between the two species.

The tail tips of these geckos exhibited an extraordinary development that instantly distinguished them and their fellow members of the genus *Lygodactylus* from all other lizards. In effect the tail tip serves as a fifth foot, holding on to the tree trunk by a series of transverse plates each of which is covered by microscopic hairlike processes. When the tail is pressed against the tree trunk, myriads of these "hairs" are inserted into every irregularity of the bark with such adhesive strength that the tail tip alone will support the entire weight of the gecko.

That is not much, of course, for the biggest of my Beira geckos was under three inches in length, the tail constituting the greater part. Like the body it was colored in drab tones of gray or olive, flecked or streaked with darker and lighter markings all subject to chameleon-like change so as to harmonize with the bark on which the geckos dwell. There too they find the tiny beetles, ants, bugs and spiders that constitute for them their staff of life.

When I thought I had enough geckos, I struck across some wasteland toward an extensive sports ground. At intervals around its periphery were piles of dry grass scythed from the football field. Ideal for snakes, but a solitary sloughed "skin" was the sole reward for half an hour spent in turning the haycocks.

Next I made for the great landing field in whose surrounding ditch I hopefully collected a lizard of the genus I was looking for, but it was not the right species. A plane zoomed down as I worked my way around the drome toward distant coconut palms growing on low sand dunes. Piled palm fronds appeared promising but yielded nothing, so, with my eager expectations unrealized, I tramped back to the hotel which I reached in time for a few consoling cups of tea.

The following morning we set out in search of the little Anglican church that had been erected as a memorial to the British residents of Mozambique who had given their lives in the war of 1914-1918. Outside was a reminder that we were in Africa, the notice board informing us that evensong would be held at ·W·ꟼ ⅁ᔭ:6 Clearly the pasting on of the time slip had been left to a Native with topsy-turvy notions.

Monday morning was fully occupied at the customs and in trying to obtain information about the missing truck. Mr. Barnett, of the clearing and forwarding agency, assured me that both it and the two shipments of equipment had been railed weeks ago. There were unavoidable delays at the Shire where both goods and vehicles had to be ferried across the swollen river to be transferred to a train on the north bank, but he was confident I would find everything awaiting me at Blantyre.

There was no time to lose if I was to secure the two *Mabuya* lizards before leaving Beira. So immediately after lunch Mary, Billy and I boarded a bus and asked for tickets to the terminus of its route. This happened to be the suburb of Miramar, something of a seaside resort in season. We walked north along the almost deserted beach. The waves brought to my feet a dead fish which I saved for the museum, after removing from its mouth a hook that I gave to one of several small urchins, each of whom had staked out a short stretch of shore in which to fish with a bent pin. Near by a Native woman was standing knee-deep in the surf while she groped for clams with both hands. She appeared quite expert at the job, tossing the shellfish ashore for her little daughter to gather into a basket. The temperature was very pleasant as a strong breeze off the ocean mitigated the warmth of the sun, and great rollers broke upon the steeper sections of the beach.

Leaving Mary and Billy to revel in the beauty of their surroundings while reclining against a sandbank, I departed in search of the lizards. Presently I came to a huge and shabby bull ring whose immediate vicinity was noisome in the extreme. Among the litter were many planks and scraps of galvanized iron; these I overturned circumspectly but without avail. From some low bushes dashed a lizard, destined to disturb me for the rest of my days as I but glimpsed it departing and failed to recognize the species. Time and again I stole back to the spot but without seeing the reptile.

Abandoning the search I wandered on through waist-high grass till I came out on the far side of a field where a dozen Natives were cutting hay. When I mentioned snakes they led me to the corpse of a harmless House-Snake (*Boaedon l. lineatus*) they had killed a few hours before. Lying in the sun had not improved it; but a snake is a snake however odoriferous, so I salvaged it and dropped sixpence upon the palm of its astonished slayer.

All hands abandoned work to accompany me, unsolicited, to the edge of the field where a score of uprooted stumps were lying. Each required two or more fellows to overturn it. By all past standards a bag of snakes should have resulted, but not so much as a lizard did we see. Something was definitely amiss with Mozambique. At this juncture I discovered the loss of my favorite forceps; followed by the boys I slowly retraced my steps to where I had emerged from the rank grass. No sign of the forceps. Disconsolately I returned to the beach en route for Miramar, but when Mary heard of my loss she proposed we have another look. I felt it was hopeless but she was eager to find them, so back we went to the hayfield. Hardly had we covered fifty yards when an exclamation from Mary caused me to turn—she was pointing to the five-inch forceps lying among the hay where they had fallen.

Instead of taking the bus at Miramar we continued on along the beach all the way to Beira, where we had tea at the Emporium. Then to the Hotel Avenida for our baggage and on through the gathering dusk to the station. Up and down the thronged platform the others might saunter, but for the naturalist there is no respite. Behind drawn blinds in the stifling carriage I took from my suitcase a scalpel, scissors and can of alcohol. Then I proceeded to degut the smelly serpent, labeling and pickling it and other trophies before returning the tin to my suitcase. This time-consuming task took fully half an hour during every moment of which I feared the guard or a passenger would open the door and ask for an explanation in Portuguese!

"Dinner will be served in the restaurant car shortly after leaving Beira," announced the attendant. But Mary declared she did not want any dinner so only Billy and I went along to the diner, a most depressing grubby place where a dozen men were sundowning. Seated at a table we waited with slowly growing impatience. The guard came through collecting passports that would be returned to us at the frontier. By way of exchange he gave us declaration forms to be filled in by those leaving Portuguese territory. We made the attempt but had to abandon it, so violently was the train rocking. As it gathered speed dust whirled about us and feeling that dinner would be impossible under such conditions we returned to the compartment.

Encountering the guard in the corridor I asked him what time we would reach Blantyre. "Seven," said he abruptly, hurrying on. "Seven A.M.," I mused. "They *have* speeded things up; what a difference bridging the Zambezi has made." In a guidebook of the 1930's I had read of the exasperating delays attending the ferrying of passengers across the great Zambezi. In those days the 349-mile journey from Beira to Blantyre took twenty-four hours; it would seem as if the old schedule had been halved. Pretty good going for an African train—around twenty-six miles per hour; no wonder we were receiving such a shaking. Rejoining the others I gave them the news. Mary was skeptical. I was willing to concede that quite likely they might not be up to time, but we would do well to be ready and should rise fairly early.

Presently there was a knock on the door and in came a grimy Native with three great bundles of bedding. He proceeded to make up the beds allowing sheets and blankets to drag on the dusty floor. No great matter, perhaps, for as soon as the lower beds were made up he stood on them in his bare feet the better to reach the upper bunk and hang its mosquito net. In this were three major holes through which a human fist could be passed with ease. Later, when the guard arrived to collect the charges on the bedding, I asked if he could not furnish better nets. He replied that all were old and in similar condition. This was scarcely correct for there was only one hole as large as mine in Mary's net. Into two of them I thrust my sports stockings, then closed the third with my pillow to forestall visits by the notorious malaria-bearing mosquitoes of Zambezia.

In the course of that disturbed night the train seemed to be continually stopping to the accompaniment of an astonishing amount of shunting and shouting. During these halts baggage-seeking Europeans and Africans would hurry along the corridor or stand outside the window talking loudly as they met or parted from old friends. In a way I enjoyed listening to the babel, though I could understand neither Portuguese, Sena, nor other local languages. As, none too comfortable in shirt and shorts, I tossed and turned, I consoled myself by saying: "This is Africa, it *is* good to be back."

At dawn an African attendant arrived with stout cups of good hot coffee. We drew up with a jolt and I looked out to verify what I already suspected. The station showed we were still in Portuguese territory and had not even crossed the Zambezi!

On the platform was an old Zanzibari pleased to meet someone who knew his island as he was homesick for his Nguja-kuu. He had come to Sena in 1905 and "having no money, married" a local woman and settled down. Now, with a growing family, he was poorer than ever. He inquired what I was doing and on hearing that we were going on safari, suggested I should take him with us. Had I acquiesced he might well have boarded the train then and there, shouting to his friends a few farewell instructions for his wife. Apparently he felt that "going places" offered at least a temporary solution of his problems.

A few minutes later we were rumbling across the then longest bridge in the world, the Zambezi bridge being over two and a quarter miles (12,064 feet) in length, consequently surpassing the Tay Bridge in Scotland or the Sone Bridge in India. Looking down on the swollen swirling waters, so laden with the rich red soil of Africa that they seemed like mud, I marveled at the engineering feat that had planted the 35 main piers at a depth of 120 feet in the river bed, then raised them thirty-two feet above the highest recorded flood level. Exclusive of its single track, the structural steel involved is estimated to be 17,000 tons, while the concrete amounted to about 95,750 cubic yards.

No sooner were we safely across than our train stopped at the small station of Mutarara to discharge some freight. After this had been accomplished in the usual leisurely fashion, the whistle blew for passengers to clamber on board again presumably to continue the journey. Instead the train ran smoothly backward down the line and out onto the bridge where it came to rest. I concluded that considerate authority, proud of the only spectacle along the route worth looking at, was providing passengers with a second chance. Gladly we availed ourselves, going out on the observation platform to admire the color contrasts of silvery-white sand bars and islets smothered in rich green papyrus surrounded by the reddish-brown flood. Of wildlife there was little—here and there a solitary heron or party of snowy egrets—but not a crocodile to be seen. When one of the train crew joined us on the platform I inquired how long we were likely to remain; only then did I learn that the procedure was routine practice to enable the engine to get her wind before tackling the long gradient beyond Mutarara.

In due course, the first set of forms having been collected and our passports returned, we were issued with fresh documents for the

Nyasaland Customs and Department of Immigration respectively. Perhaps the underlying idea was to relieve the tedium of the journey through interminable dry scrub and savanna by keeping us occupied. Whatever the reason, the mental exercise of all this form-filling was having a beneficial effect; offhand I could say how old I was without any finger work, no longer was it necessary to ask Mary if I was married or single, and I blessed parental foresight that had given me but one Christian name to "Please print in full block capitals."

These documents we presented in person to a young customs-cum-immigration officer in an open shed at Port Herald on the River Shire. About thirty miles up the line we arrived at the junction of the Shire and Ruo Rivers where the Chiromo bridge had been swept away some months before. The guard came along telling everyone to leave their suitcases in the carriages and walk up the line to one of two paddle steamers. Our luggage, he said, would be transported to the steamer in due course.

After a considerable lapse of time a long line of Africans appeared, each man bearing on his head a varied assortment of hand baggage. With sure-footed ease most of them strode out along a temporary pier of scaffolding, constructed of balks of timber, and deposited their loads on the deck of our steamer close to where I was leaning over the rail. One fellow, however, with three suitcases balanced on his head, stood hesitantly. When told to "hurry up" he rather clumsily attempted to remove the suitcases. Off shot the topmost one down between the balks, striking against one of them so that, deflected, it fell across the lowest beam a mere foot or two above the swirling waters of the Shire. From this precarious perch it was rescued and safely brought up by the bearer. Some passenger was more fortunate than he or she realized.

Tired of waiting for the vessel to cast off, we sought out seats beneath an awning. Next to me sat an elderly man about whose face there was something strangely familiar. Presently we engaged in conversation and I discovered he was Leslie Tarlton, whom I had last seen in Nairobi in 1919. Readers of Theodore Roosevelt's *African Game Trails* will recall that Tarlton was one of those who accompanied the ex-President on his big game hunt in 1910. At that time Tarlton was credited with having shot more lions than anyone else in British East Africa. Now, seventy-one years of age, but game as ever, he was on his way to visit a nephew living at the foot of Mlanje Mountain. After we had all settled in the train, waiting on the far side of the Shire, Tarlton came to our carriage and relieved the tedium of the journey with tales of recent happenings in Kenya Colony.

As the train puffed slowly up the last few miles to Limbe the sun sank down in a panoply of pink and golden glory, then switched off the light. Young Africans who had come rushing down from their huts to cheer and wave continued to do so undaunted by darkness, the babel of their voices rising to a crescendo, then fading away as we chugged on. With the setting of the sun had come a most welcome drop in temperature for, to its credit, the railway had raised us 3,810 feet by the time we reached Limbe station. There, before going on to Blantyre, we were scheduled to remain for an hour or two while all heavy baggage was removed from the wagon sealed at Beira customs for transit through Portuguese territory. Happily we were spared this long wait for we were met by a chauffeur from Ryall's Hotel who speedily drove us over the six remaining miles to Blantyre—at that time the only stretch of macadamized road in all Nyasaland.

This arrangement enabled us to freshen up after the dusty journey and yet be in time to sit down to a dinner to which we did ample justice. Each of our rooms, being in the new wing, had its own modern bathroom. To a travel-weary trio this was an unexpected treat and, tired out, I for one slept soundly until daybreak.

II

Ulendo Preparations—
Midnight Fire

O NE of my primary requirements was a large
room or lockup shed in which I could unpack our camping equipment and the stores that must be assembled in smaller loads suitable
for *ulendo*—as a safari is called in Nyasaland. When I broached the
subject to the hotel management, they not only had nothing to offer
but informed me apologetically that in Blantyre, as elsewhere, hotel
accommodation was in short supply and my party could not remain
for more than three days! I also learned that the car had been sent
to meet us at Limbe at the suggestion of Mr. W. E. H. Rangeley,
commissioner for the Blantyre district, to whom we were already in-
debted for the warning telegram regarding the truck.

We were at breakfast when the energetic Mr. Rangeley called in
to say that he would be occupied by committees and sundry en-
gagements until 11:00 A.M., after which he would be glad to discuss
various matters pertaining to our plans. Meanwhile there were
plenty of other things to be done.

Our first call was at Hall's Garage to enquire about the truck,
dispatched from New York exactly five months before. It had
reached Limbe, we learned, and might be expected in Blantyre
within the next few days. Of the two shipments of stores and equipment from Boston and Glasgow, however, nothing was known. I

had better inquire for them at the railway customs office at the other end of town. But the customs clerk denied all knowledge of the shipments for which he had received no waybills. While he was endeavoring to get through to customs headquarters at Limbe on the telephone, a Goanese assistant came in to say that he fancied he had found everything in the goods shed. Returning with him I recognized most of the Boston items among a vast mountain of goods. Beside them were several huge bundles sewn up in sacking that I supposed was the tentage from Glasgow, for had I not Mr. Barnett's assurance I would find both Boston and Glasgow shipments awaiting me at Blantyre? Assuming that all was well I departed in search of the district commissioner's office.

No one could have been more helpful than Mr. Rangeley. Cutting all manner of formalities he issued me with gun permits and other licenses. To expedite the licensing of the truck and granting of a driving license to Billy he accompanied me to the Police Department. I explained my need of a spacious lockup place to which to transfer the shipments. Rangeley promptly drove me to several scattered buildings whose owners might be willing to rent them to me for a week. But everywhere we met with the same answer; godowns were filled with tobacco and the housing shortage was as acute for goods as for people.

Rangeley then suggested his own garage, saying his car could remain in the open, but he feared his place was too far from town for the proposal to be practicable. However, if it would facilitate matters he would be glad to put me up so that I would be on the spot. He would drive me out that afternoon to see if the garage was suitable and arrange that the four "boys" he had collected should be there to meet me.

On previous safaris, which had begun a thousand miles to the north of Blantyre, I had always had a nucleus of my own old boys with which to start. In Nyasaland, where I was a complete stranger and where Swahili was understood by few, it might have taken me weeks to assemble a satisfactory staff that would work well together. To have them gathered for me by someone on the spot was a great boon.

The cook and the headboy, remarked Rangeley, as we drove

along, were a bit old for *ulendo* but this drawback was offset by their known honesty, both having been for many years in the employ of a senior government official now on leave. He was expected back in four or five months, at which time I must release them as they were on half-pay during their employer's absence. This not too satisfactory arrangement would at least give me time to look around and arrange for replacements for the last few months of the *ulendo*.

Their homes were in faraway Fort Johnston on Lake Nyasa, said Rangeley, for both were of the Yao tribe, a people of superior intelligence who generally make good servants as they are quick to learn. On the other hand, they are notoriously temperamental, very superstitious, and the younger generation are deficient in the courtesy that was so marked a characteristic of the old people. Well, my future associates were certainly old enough; the kindly face of Amini, our cook-to-be, was almost wizened, his hair white. That I did not know till later for, as befitted a Mahommedan, he wore a fez and his lean figure was concealed beneath a white *kanzu*, that night-shirt-like garment so popular with Moslems. Beside him stood Hamisi, a shorter, thickset fellow wearing European clothes topped by a black velvet cap of the flat-crowned type worn by elderly Indian baboos.

With justifiable pride they said they had been with their present employer for twenty years. While there were reassuring aspects to such a record, so long an association is likely to result in a devotion to the ways of the old master that is resistant to changes desired by the new one. Hamisi introduced his nephew Thomas, a well-built, glum-looking fellow whose expression changed remarkably when at his ease. Thomas, said Hamisi, would be assistant tent boy under his tutelage as headboy; he was acquainted with the duties for he had been a personal servant with the Vernay Expedition of the American Museum of Natural History and understood a little Swahili. I asked to see his book and noted he had done nothing for the past nine months. My misgivings aroused, I inquired of Rangeley what he thought about it. He questioned Thomas, then told me the fellow claimed to have been resting at home; this might, or might not, have some significance. Such vacations, I learned, were by no means an uncommon occurrence since wages had soared, not too greatly to meet the increased cost of living in the towns perhaps, but providing relatively princely spending power in the more remote villages.

Finally there was Patrick, who pronounced his name so like "Padre" that I wrote him down as such, a cause of merriment to Thomas who for some days dubbed him Padre Patrick. Thickset and sullen, Patrick appeared more suitable to the tasks of an agricultural laborer than a skinner, which was what he aspired to be. He was a Nyanja from near-by Chiradzulu, spoke no language but his own—which placed him at the mercy of companions who must translate his every request—and had never before worked for a white man. In his favor were his youth, sturdy build and strength, all considerable assets when one reflected on the lorry-loading potentials of the elderly Amini and Hamisi. As the latter, translating, informed Patrick that he would be accepted on trial, the worried sullen expression gave way to a not unpleasing smile. I told him I hoped he would always look that way for I wanted our *ulendo* to be a holiday even if we had to work hard.

Rangeley drove me back to town where I had promised to accompany Hall's representative to the customs to assist in clearing the consignments. This proved a tedious and protracted business though only one shipment was involved, for, to my consternation, I now discovered that the tentage, lamps and bale of boys' blankets had not arrived after all. These items were absolute essentials without which I could not start on Monday as planned, and in Africa unless one works to schedule whole days drift past on the ocean of time. So to the railway and customs authorities at Limbe appealing telephone calls were put through urging that the missing items be traced and forwarded with expedition.

As the only other hotel in Blantyre was as full as Ryall's, accommodation for M. & B. had been secured at Mrs. Purse's boarding-house to which, after breakfast next morning, they and their suitcases departed in a taxi. A busy day lay ahead of them, for walking about humid and hilly Blantyre was particularly trying as the unsurfaced roads were deep in dust that rose in choking clouds with every passing car and truck. Of these there were many; indeed, except for ourselves, few except Africans appeared to walk about town. Billy had to be photographed for her driving license. This was to be followed by a practice drive around town which she, never having driven a lorry before, anticipated with eager trepidation.

The Dodge truck had arrived at last and the English mechanic who fetched it from the station was most enthusiastic over the model, saying it was the best he had ever seen. We all went to view the lorry for ourselves and found it parked near the garage. It certainly looked a beauty with its dark green paint shining in the African sun. To see it thus one would never imagine it had traveled so far, besides having spent idle months in Beira while waiting for a train. The stake sides were so constructed that any section could be removed if we wished to get at something without off-loading everything. Its reinforced frame would enable us to "safely load 8,500 pounds of cargo," Chryslers had said. There was ample room for the three of us in the wonderfully springy seat of the de luxe lockup cab, whose only key had been found wedged in the tread of one of the dual rear tires!

At ports on the outward voyage I had often leaned upon the rail to watch the cargo being brought up in nets from the depths of the vessel, the contents creaking, grinding, and occasionally crashing against the sides of the hold. On such occasions I was assailed by misgivings as to how much would survive of the shipment I had packed with such care in Cambridge long months before. Consequently there was an added zest to unpacking when I found everything was intact, undoubtedly due in part to the metal strapping nailed around the crates by Maxwell French at the museum. The only thing broken in the entire consignment was an old safari teapot that had been cracked for twenty years; it had at last succumbed to jarring. Work on these stores kept me fully occupied from dawn till late at night during two entire days, for I was determined to have everything ready by Saturday night.

Rangeley, as I had already discovered, was keenly interested in natural history, and I spent an enjoyable evening listening to my host's experiences and anecdotes of animal life which he related with delightful vim. When his other guest, Guy Muldoon, arrived, Rangeley persuaded him to describe for my benefit his method of "fishing" for lions at Nchisi, a technique I was later to see him apply.

I remarked that the manager of the Standard Bank had offered to have forwarded any mail that should come for us if addressed care of the bank. Someone else had urged me to take advantage of this offer and discontinue having letters sent "Poste Restante, Blantyre," as the African postal personnel were notoriously careless in the matter of forwarding to frequently changing addresses. Rangeley then told me that some of the employees at Zomba Post Office were awaiting trial for lightly canceling the picturesque shilling stamps so much used on air mail; then removing them from the envelopes and destroying the letters. Allegedly they were sold to someone in Zomba who was buying attractive Nyasa stamps from all the Native clerks in town. The stamps were then resold to dealers in the United States from whom the vendor was said to be receiving $140 a month. Discovery had come through Mrs. Colby, wife of His Excellency the Governor, recognizing in a roadside ditch some partly destroyed letters that she had sent to post.

Next morning Rangeley drove me to town that I might call on Mary and Billy whom I had not seen for two days. I found they had had quite an adventure during the night. Mary awoke about 3:30 A.M. hearing voices, which she at first supposed were those of people returning from a dance being held in connection with the annual Agricultural Show. Then a woman called out: there was the sound of scurrying feet in the corridor, and Mary could hear the bathroom taps running.

"Billy, are you awake?" inquired Mary softly, then: "Wake up, people are running about. I think there's a fire and we'd better get up."

Billy was first to the door. As she opened it a man said: "May I have your pail?" rushed in, grabbed it, and was gone.

Billy seized the water jug and Mary followed with the bottle of drinking water, there being nothing else left to take! The sitting room was filled with smoke, for the davenport was blazing. Mary snatched a smoldering cushion and tossed it through an open casement, happily missing a car parked on the driveway just outside. After the davenport had been subjected to more dowsing it was carried into the garden by some of the Native staff.

It was thought the fire had been started by a cigarette. Fortunately, a glass door permitted the reflected glow to be seen by a lady boarder who rose to investigate and gave the alarm. Otherwise the house might well have been burned to the ground for there was no fire engine in all Blantyre.

We fell to discussing plans for the morrow, for much remained to be done. Billy had to collect prints of her photograph, take them to the police for her driving licence, collect the lorry and drive to the Shell agents to pick up a forty-five-gallon drum of gasoline. This we would never have got but for the friendly intervention of the indispensable Mr. Rangeley, for gasoline was in very short supply owing to the cutting of the Haifa pipeline. Only after Billy had done these jobs could she proceed to the district commissioner's garage to pick up the loads and me. After that we would make one last call at the station to see if the tents had arrived.

Though Billy turned up with the lorry at ten-thirty next morning, it was noon before we got back to town. The tents had not come, but the stationmaster thought they would surely be on a train due in the next morning. If they were not, Rangeley, whom I went to see after lunch, promised to lend us his tent for a few weeks and said he would phone Mlanje Boma and ask the commissioner there if we might borrow his also. It seemed best to postpone our departure until the morning, for by this time it was so late it would be dark before we could reach Mlanje.

The Purses obligingly agreed to put up a camp bed in the lounge for me, where the deceased davenport so recently reposed. We learned that instead of fire they had suffered a minor flood during the afternoon. To conserve the dwindling water supply the municipality had been shutting off the flow for stated periods. As a conservation measure it had hardly proved a success at the Purses for one of their houseboys had left a kitchen tap turned on when he found no water in it. The kitchen was deserted in midafternoon when the supply came on again. "All we now lack is the pestilence," remarked Billy pessimistically.

Billy parked the loaded lorry on the driveway and some of our boys were told to sleep on it to prevent pilfering. The lounge was vacated by 10:00 P.M. and shortly afterward I was sound asleep beside the open casements. I awoke with a start, certain that someone had run a hand over my feet. In an effort to free myself of the